Where Does It Go?

Written by Babs Bell Hajdusiewicz

Illustrated by E. Silas Smith

Dominie Press, Inc.

Dedication

**To the many special people
in my life
who have encouraged me
to ask questions.**

Published by

Dominie Press, Inc.
5945 Pacific Center Boulevard
San Diego, California 92121 USA

ISBN 1-56270-496-6
Printed in Singapore by PH Productions.

1 2 3 4 5 6 7 PH 98 97 96

Where does it go? 3

The milk goes in the refrigerator.

Where does it go?

The glass goes in the sink.

Where does it go?

The napkin goes in the trash can.

Where does it go?

The hot pad goes in the drawer.

Where does it go?

12   The placemat goes in the cupboard.

Where does it go? 13

The pizza goes in me!

Dear Parent,

This book will help your child enjoy reading. As the story is read, your child will come to see that an answer to a question often depends on the situation.

Help your child use the picture above each question to predict an answer. You'll want to encourage and praise any idea that your child offers. For example, you might say, "That's a good idea." Or say, "You think. . ." and then repeat what your child has said.

Encourage further discussion by asking your child, "Why do you think that?" Then invite your child to turn the page to check the prediction. Discuss why the prediction or the story's answer makes sense—or doesn't make sense.

When you and your child talk about the story, your child comes to see that words printed in a book are like words people use when they talk. Here are some ways you can encourage discussion about this book's story:

- Ask a story-related question that cannot be answered by a simple yes or no. Here are some examples:
  - ? Why does milk go in the refrigerator?
  - ? What things go in your refrigerator?
  - ? What happens to the pizza after the boy eats it?
- Tell how the story reminds you of something you've seen or done.
- Look for opportunities to use the story's words. Talk about the story's ideas as you and your child go about routine activities, such as cooking or getting dressed.

Happy Reading!

Tip: It is good when your child likes to read a favorite book again and again. Here's why:

- Your child likes the story — its ideas, the pictures, the sounds of the words.
- Your child likes the good feeling of reading a book whose words and pictures are familiar.
- Your child wants to see if a book's words and pictures look the same every time.
- Your child wants to know the story — to "own" and use the story's words and ideas in daily living.
- Your child likes this special time with you!

The Questions & Answers Series

Blue Set

- What Hangs From the Tree?
- What Plays Music?
- Who Has Wings?
- Who Can Hop?
- Which Is Heavier?
- Why Do I Feel Safe?
- Where Does It Go?
- How Do I Feel?
- When Do Cars Stop?
- Who Lives Here?
- Who Works Here?
- How Can I Help?

Written by Babs Bell Hajdusiewicz

Illustrated by E. Silas Smith